Chapter 1

Disney

TOY STORY

"THE MYSTERIOUS STRANGER"

Disney Pocket Stories

Panini Publishing

...y: Dan Jolley
...by: Chris Moreno
Colours by: Veronica Gandini, Andrew Dalhouse & Flavio B.Silva
Letters: Deron Bennett

Editor: Paul Morrissey
Trade Editor: Aaron Sparrow
Cover Artists: Mike Decarlo, Marcio Takara, Michael Cavallaro & Brent Schoonover

HURRY UP, ANDY! WE DON'T WANT TO BE LATE!
AWW, MOM, I DON'T WANNA GO TO THIS THING ANYWAY!
WELL, YOU ARE GOING--WE ALL ARE--SO GET A MOVE ON.

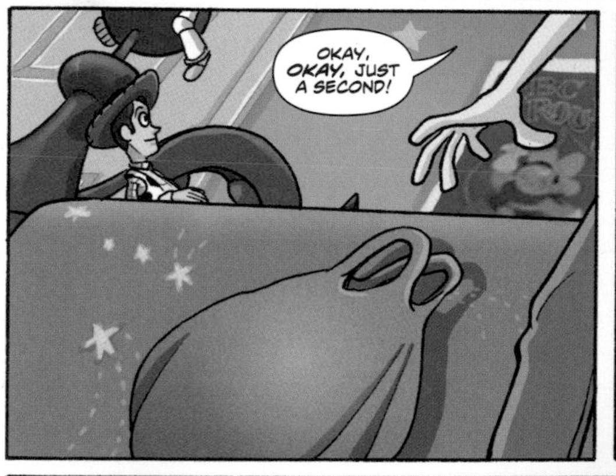
OKAY, OKAY, JUST A SECOND!

HOW LONG'S IT S'POSED TO TAKE, ANYWAY?

I DON'T KNOW. HOW LONG DOES IT TAKE A BUNCH OF LITTLE GIRLS TO DANCE?

SO, BUZZ... WHAT IS THAT THING? FRIEND OF YOURS?
SORRY, WOODY...

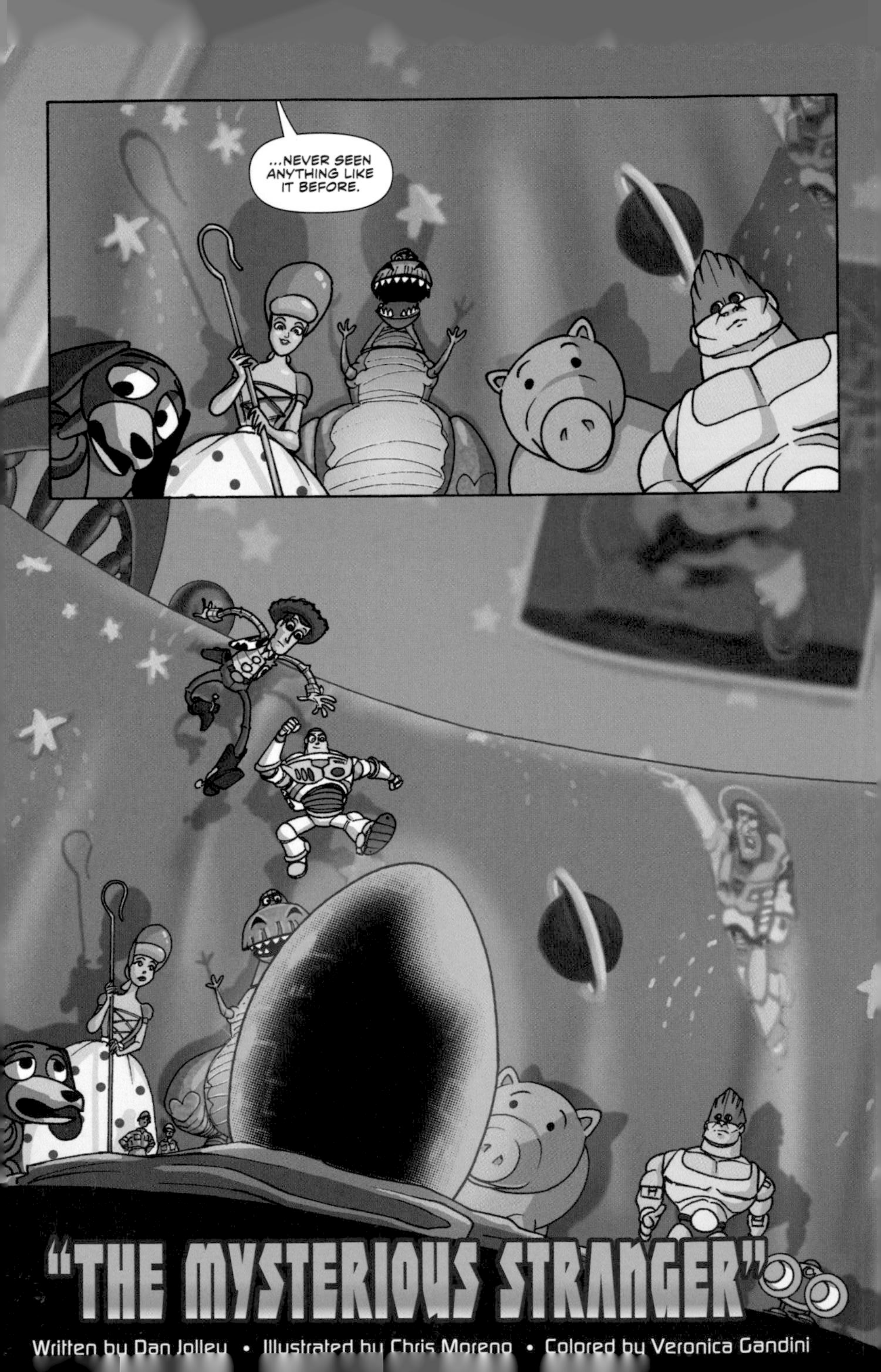
...NEVER SEEN ANYTHING LIKE IT BEFORE.
"THE MYSTERIOUS STRANGER"
Written by Dan Jolley • Illustrated by Chris Moreno • Colored by Veronica Gandini

I JUST FIGURED, SINCE IT'S ALL FUTURISTIC-LOOKING...
WHAT, I'M SUPPOSED TO KNOW EVERY SCIENCE-FICTION TOY OUT THERE? DO YOU KNOW EVERY COWBOY OUT THERE?
NO HARM IN ASKING.
WE SHOULD PROBABLY FOCUS MORE ON DAMAGE CONTROL FIRST.

...YEAH. THIS IS LIABLE TO CAUSE SOME REAL TROUBLE.
IT'S SO SHINY.
WHAT DO YOU THINK IT IS, SARGE?
TOO LITTLE INFORMATION TO TELL! MA'AM!

I DON'T LIKE IT. WHY'S IT JUST SITTING THERE? WHY DOESN'T IT SAY STOMETHING?
IT'S PROBABLY TOO SCARED. I KNOW I WOULD BE, IF THE FIRST THING I SAW WAS YOUR FACE.

OKAY, LISTEN UP, EVERYONE!
OBVIOUSLY ANDY'S MADE A NEW ADDITION TO THE ROOM--AND I KNOW HOW TOUCHY SOME OF US ARE ABOUT THAT KIND OF THING--
--BUT THERE'S NO NEED TO GET EXCITED!

WHOEVER THIS MYSTERIOUS STRANGER IS, I'M SURE HE'S JUST AS NERVOUS ABOUT MEETING US AS WE ARE ABOUT MEETING HIM.
SO LET ME BE THE FIRST ONE TO SAY: WELCOME TO ANDY'S ROOM, FRIEND! I'M WOODY.
WHAT'S *YOUR* NAME?

MAYBE WE'RE EXPECTING TOO MUCH CONVERSATION FROM AN EGG.
WELL...IT CAN'T BE JUST AN *EGG*. CAN IT? ANDY WOULDN'T WANT TO PLAY WITH A...WITH AN *EGG*. I MEAN, SERIOUSLY.
IT'S AN **EGG.**

I BET IT'S A ROBOT!
A ROBOT?
YEAH! THE KIND THAT, Y'KNOW, ***FOLDS UP!*** IT'S JUST ***FOLDED UP*** INTO AN EGG!

OR...
THERE MIGHT BE A TOY *INSIDE* IT.
LOTS OF TOYS COME IN EGGS, DON'T THEY?

EXCUSE ME--IS THERE ANYBODY IN THERE?
CAN YOU HEAR ME?
...HELLO?

HMPH.
IF YOU ASK ME, THAT'S ONE *UPPITY* EGG.

OOOH, I CAN'T STAND NOT KNOWING!
WHAT IF IT'S SOME NEW KIND OF TOY? WHAT IF IT'S SOMETHING WE DON'T EVEN KNOW ABOUT?
NOW, REX, CALM DOWN...
SHOVE

THIS COULD BE WHAT WE'VE ALL BEEN SCARED OF! I KNOW I'M SCARED.

ETCH!
SHOW 'EM WHAT I MEAN!

SEE? SEE? WHAT IF IT MAKES PICTURES RIGHT IN THE AIR?
HOW COULD ETCH COMPETE WITH THAT?

ALL RIGHT, ALL RIGHT, LET'S ALL JUST CALM DOWN, OKAY?

I'M SURE THE NEW TOY WILL SAY HELLO WHEN IT'S GOOD AND *READY.*

PEOPLE, PEOPLE, WE SHOULDN'T BE GETTING *UPSET...*
...WE SHOULD BE FIGURING OUT HOW TO MAKE THE NEW TOY FEEL *WELCOME,* WHENEVER IT *DOES* WAKE UP.

YOU KNOW...I *COULD* PLAN A DANDY MEET-AND-GREET FOR OUR NEW FRIEND...

YOU AND YOUR MEN WOULD HELP ME STRING UP SOME DECORATIONS, WOULDN'T YOU?

MA'AM, YES MA'AM!

ARE YOU CRAZY?
WE SHOULDN'T HAVE ANYTHING TO DO WITH THIS THING!

REX, LISTEN...

YOU'RE GETTING WAY TOO WORKED UP ABOUT THIS.
WE DIDN'T KNOW ANYTHING ABOUT BUZZ WHEN HE FIRST GOT HERE, EITHER.
BUT THIS IS TOTALLY DIFFERENT!

WE DID KNOW ABOUT BUZZ. WE'D SEEN HIS COMMERCIALS ON TV.
BUT WE DON'T KNOW ANYTHING ABOUT THIS EGG!

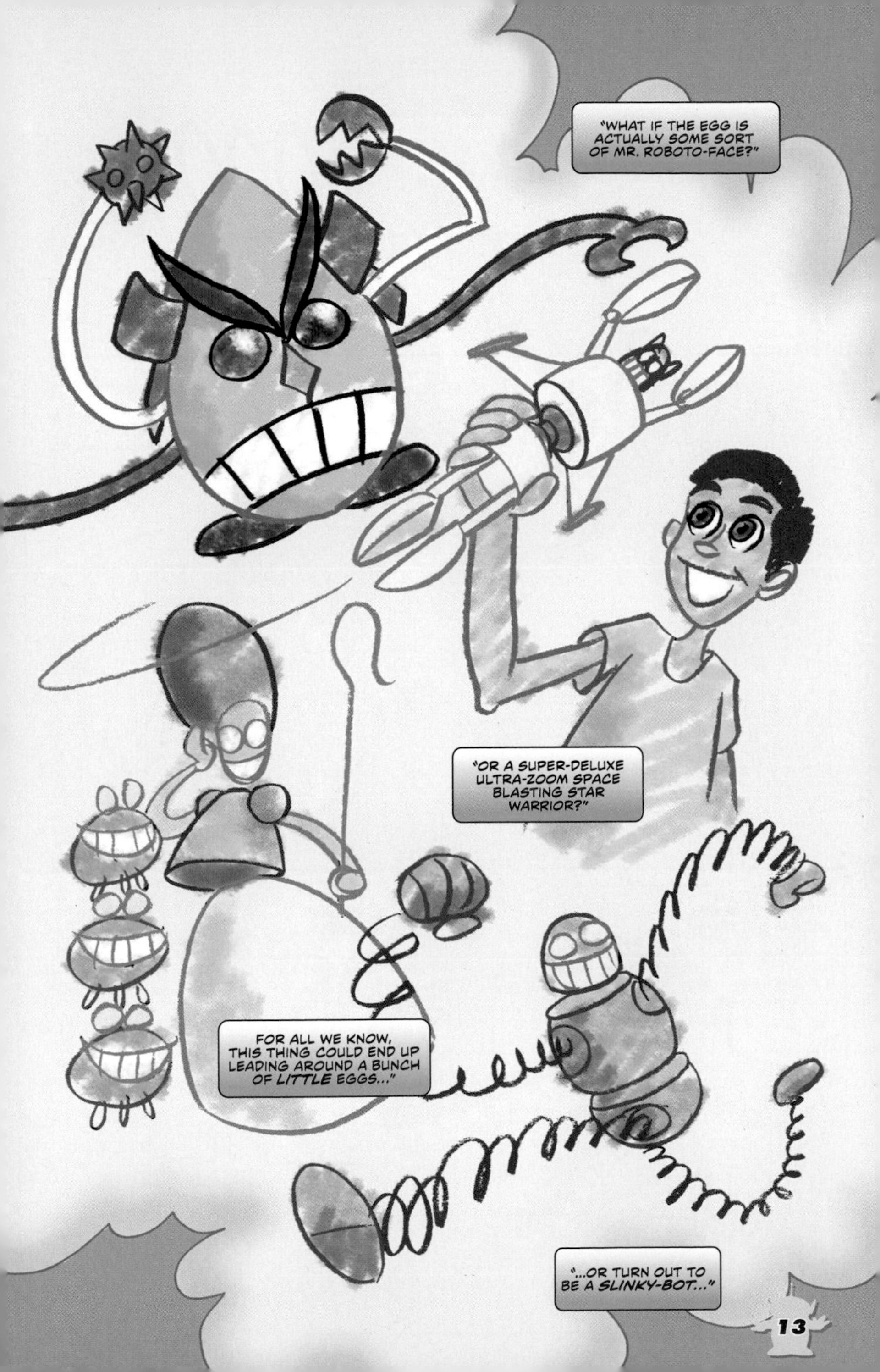
"WHAT IF THE EGG IS ACTUALLY SOME SORT OF MR. ROBOTO-FACE?"
"OR A SUPER-DELUXE ULTRA-ZOOM SPACE BLASTING STAR WARRIOR?"
FOR ALL WE KNOW, THIS THING COULD END UP LEADING AROUND A BUNCH OF *LITTLE* EGGS..."
"...OR TURN OUT TO BE A *SLINKY-BOT*..."

"...OR MAYBE EVEN THE MOST TERRIFYING ROBOTIC DINOSAUR EVER BUILT!"
NOOOOO!
I CAN'T LET ANYTHING BE SCARIER THAN ME! I JUST CAN'T!
I KNOW! I KNOW!

WE'VE ALL BEEN SCARED OF THIS OUR WHOLE LIVES!
EVERYONE'S ALWAYS TERRIFIED OF ANDY BRINGING HOME A TOY THAT'LL MAKE HIM FORGET ABOUT US!

YOU COULDN'T STAND BY AND LET THAT HAPPEN, COULD YOU, HAMM?
UH...

HOW ABOUT YOU, SLINK?
WELL, NOW, I D--

AND YOU GUYS!
MAYBE YOU CAN'T TALK, BUT WE ALL KNOW WHAT YOU'RE THINKING!

THAT EGG IS BAD!
WE HAVE TO GET RID OF IT!
WE SHOULD GET IT OUT OF THE HOUSE...MAYBE GIVE IT TO SID!

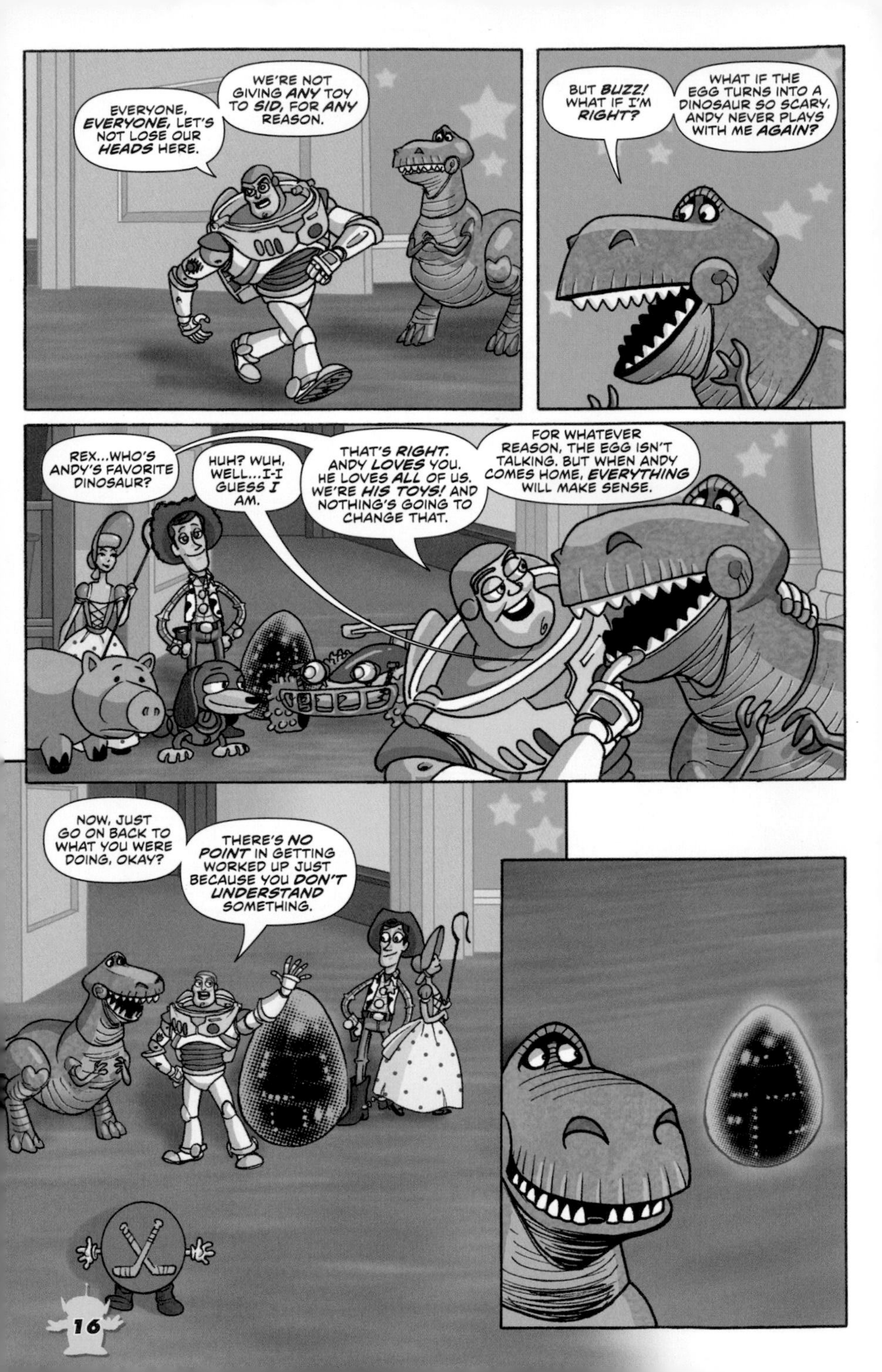
EVERYONE, EVERYONE, LET'S NOT LOSE OUR HEADS HERE.
WE'RE NOT GIVING ANY TOY TO SID, FOR ANY REASON.
BUT BUZZ! WHAT IF I'M RIGHT?
WHAT IF THE EGG TURNS INTO A DINOSAUR SO SCARY, ANDY NEVER PLAYS WITH ME AGAIN?
REX...WHO'S ANDY'S FAVORITE DINOSAUR?
HUH? WUH, WELL...I-I GUESS I AM.
THAT'S RIGHT. ANDY LOVES YOU. HE LOVES ALL OF US. WE'RE HIS TOYS! AND NOTHING'S GOING TO CHANGE THAT.
FOR WHATEVER REASON, THE EGG ISN'T TALKING. BUT WHEN ANDY COMES HOME, EVERYTHING WILL MAKE SENSE.
NOW, JUST GO ON BACK TO WHAT YOU WERE DOING, OKAY?
THERE'S NO POINT IN GETTING WORKED UP JUST BECAUSE YOU DON'T UNDERSTAND SOMETHING.

LA
LA LA LA
LAAA...

WHOOPS...!

KLONK
CLATTER
CLATTER
CLATTER
CLATTER

HOLY BRANDING IRONS!
EVERYBODY! GRAB THOSE MARBLES!

WE HAVE TO GET THEM ALL BACK IN THE JAR BEFORE ANDY COMES HOME!

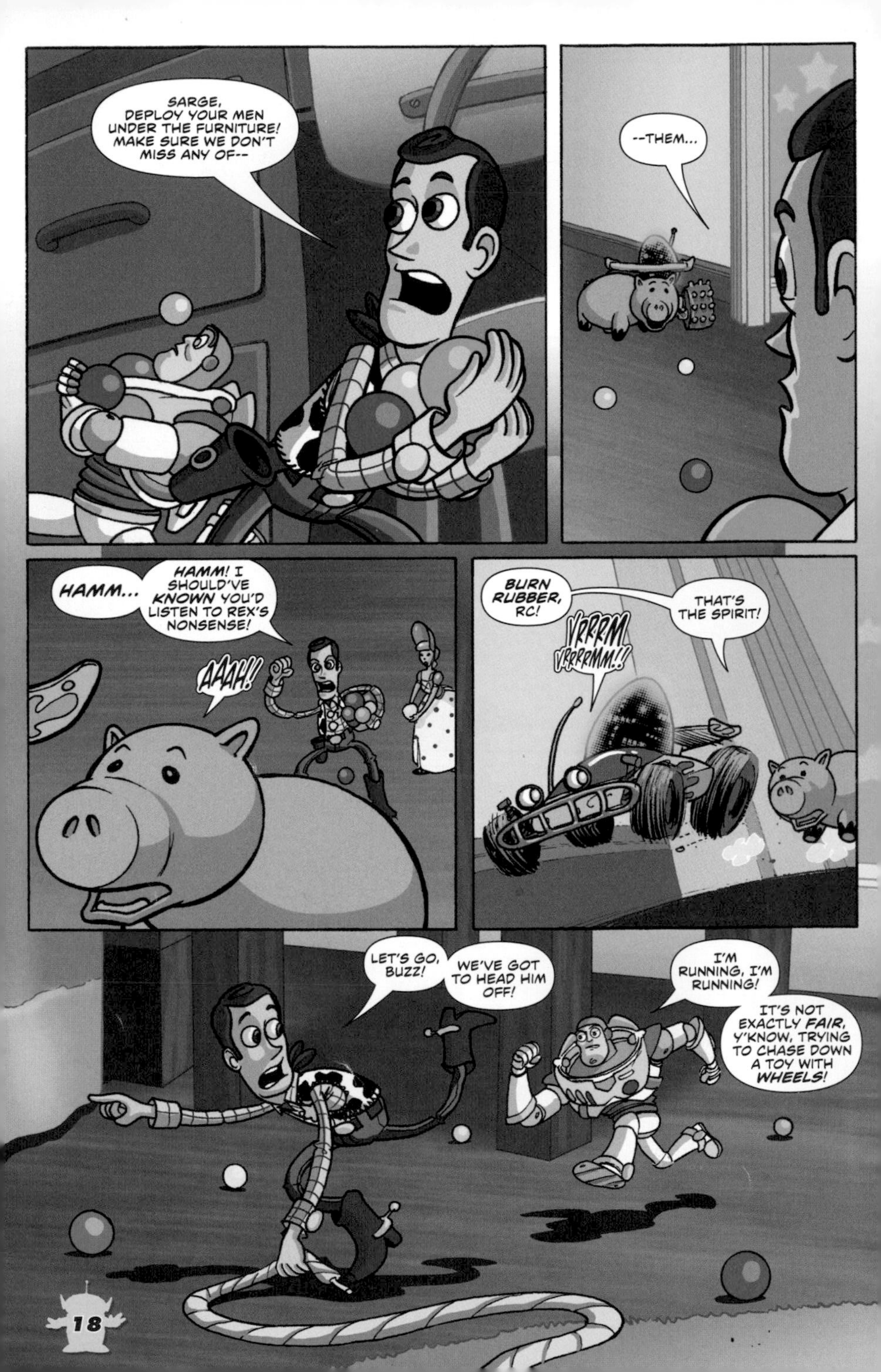
SARGE, DEPLOY YOUR MEN UNDER THE FURNITURE! MAKE SURE WE DON'T MISS ANY OF--
--THEM...
HAMM...
HAMM! I SHOULD'VE KNOWN YOU'D LISTEN TO REX'S NONSENSE!
AAAH!
BURN RUBBER, RC!
THAT'S THE SPIRIT!
VRRRM VRRRRMM!!
LET'S GO, BUZZ!
WE'VE GOT TO HEAD HIM OFF!
I'M RUNNING, I'M RUNNING!
IT'S NOT EXACTLY FAIR, Y'KNOW, TRYING TO CHASE DOWN A TOY WITH WHEELS!

OOF
I CAN'T LET YOU STOP RC!
AW, REX, COME ON...
...IT'S NOT LIKE YOU CAN HOLD US DOWN!
ANDY

I KNOW...I'M SORRY...
LET'S GO, BOYS!
FOLLOW THAT CAR!
ANDY

I SHOULD NEVER HAVE TRIED TO PLAN THIS. I'M NOT GOOD WITH PLANS!
ANDY

C'MON, RC! YOU GOTTA MOVE FASTER!

I KNOW ANDY JUST PUT FRESH BATTERIES IN YOU!
THMP
NOOO!
I CAN'T LOSE THE EGG! REX WILL BE SO DISAPPOINTED...!

HA-HA!
TO INFINITY-- AND BE--
ANDY

--YAAH!
WHAMM
I'M SORRY, BUZZ!

WE JUST CAN'T TAKE THIS KIND OF CHANCE!

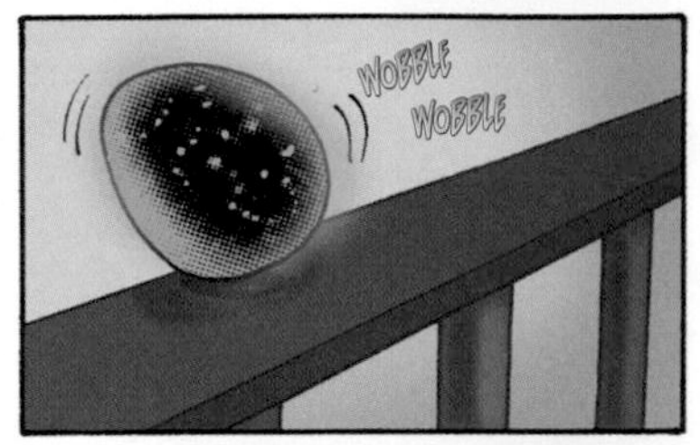
WOBBLE
WOBBLE

THAPP
I DON'T BELIEVE YOU GUYS!
THIS IS NOT HOW WE DO THINGS AROUND--

--HEEEEEERE!

FWUMP
WOW! THAT WAS A REALLY GOOD CATCH...

KLACK-A
...OHFORCRYINGOUTLOUD!
KLACK
KLACK-A
KLACK-A

RC...YOU AND I... HAVE GOT TO HAVE...A *SERIOUS* TALK...ABOUT *CAMARADERIE...*
KLACK-A
KLACK-A
KLACK-A

GOTCHA COVERED, WOODY!
YOU CAN LET GO OF THE ROPE NOW!

WHOOPS!

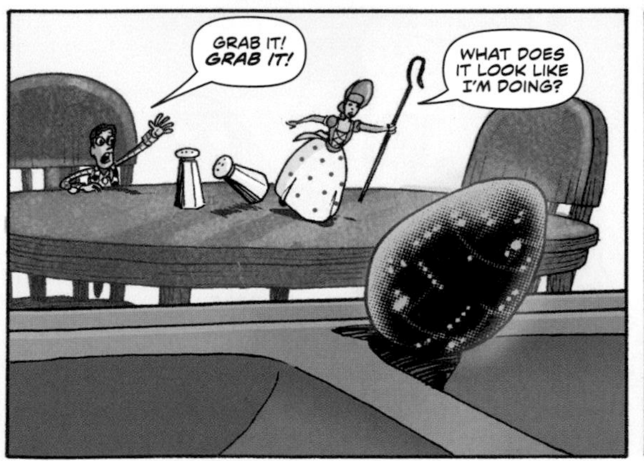
GRAB IT! *GRAB IT!*
WHAT DOES IT LOOK LIKE I'M DOING?

WHISH
WHISH
WHISH
WHISH...

OH NO YOU DON'T.

OKAY. NOW.
ANYBODY *ELSE* WANT TO TRY TO *DO IN* OUR FRIEND THE EGG?
ANYBODY?
NO?

GOOD.
THEN MAYBE YOU'LL *LISTEN* TO ME FOR A MINUTE.

LOOK, THIS EGG...IT MIGHT *BE* SOME NEW KIND OF TOY.
MAYBE IT *WILL* BE SORT OF LIKE ETCH...OR BO...
OR *YOU*, REX.

BUT WHAT IF IT TURNED OUT TO BE SOMEBODY WHO'D DO *ANYTHING* TO HELP US?
OR TOLD JOKES THAT MADE US ALL LAUGH?
MORE IMPORTANTLY...

...WHAT IF WE HAD TREATED *YOU* THE SAME WAY WHEN *YOU* FIRST GOT HERE?

DID ANY OF YOU STOP TO THINK ABOUT THAT?
YOU WERE *ALL* NEW TOYS AT ONE POINT OR ANOTHER.

LOOK, REX, WE'RE NOT ASKING YOU TO *ADOPT* THE EGG.
WE JUST WANT YOU TO GIVE IT A *CHANCE.*
YOU CAN'T FREAK OUT EVERY TIME ANDY GETS A NEW TOY.

WELL...
I GUESS I MIGHT'VE OVER-REACTED A *LITTLE*...

YEAH, AND, UH... *ABOUT* THAT--WITH THE *OVER-REACTING*... SORRY ABOUT, Y'KNOW, *TACKLING* YOU GUYS.
AND FOR DRAGGING YOU ACROSS THE FLOOR LIKE THAT.
TWICE.
YEAH, WELL, I--
VRRRM VRRM VRRRM VRRM.

THEY'RE HOME!
EVERYBODY UPSTAIRS!

GO GO GO GO!
YOU GOT THE EGG OKAY?
I GOT IT! JUST GO!

SARGE! STATUS REPORT!
THEY'RE ABOUT TO LEAVE THE GARAGE! SIR!
HURRY, PEOPLE!

OKAY, OKAY, WE MADE IT, NOW JUST GET BACK IN POSITION AND WE'LL--
OH NO!

MOVE, MOVE, WE HAVE TO GET EVERY LAST MARBLE, MOVE!

STUPID LITTLE STUPID THING...
...IT'S NOT THAT BAD, MAYBE I'M NOT PERFECT, BUT IT'S NOT THAT BAD.

THERE. HOPE SHE'S HAPPY NOW.

SPFFF

NOW, SEE? DOESN'T YOUR ROOM ALREADY SMELL SO MUCH BETTER?
IT DIDN'T STINK TO BEGIN WITH!
...WE'LL JUST AGREE TO DISAGREE ON THAT ONE.

C'MON, I'LL BET YOU'D LIKE SOME MILK AND COOKIES.
STINKY ROOM OR NOT, YOU BEHAVED VERY WELL AT THE RECITAL.
CHOCOLATE CHUNK?
CHOCOLATE CHUNK.

SO...IT'S...AN AIR FRESHENER.

SO, REX, STILL WORRIED ABOUT GETTING REPLACED?
OH, BOY. HERE IT COMES.
YOU DON'T SMELL THAT BAD. I DON'T THINK.
MAYBE IF YOU STARTED WEARING COLOGNE.

OOOH!
COULD COLOGNE MAKE ME SCARIER?
THE END

BUZZ
WOODY
LASER
SPACE RANGER
LIGHTYEAR

Chapter 2

KLICK
KLICK
KLICK
KLICK

THERE WE GO.

AND WHEN I TURN THIS...

...YES! A WORKING MODEL!
THIS'LL WIN FIRST PRIZE FOR SURE!

ANDY! COME TO DINNER!
ALREADY?
IF YOU WANT TO GET THERE BY SEVEN, WE'VE GOTTA EAT NOW!
OKAY! BE RIGHT DOWN!

WE'VE GOT TO EAT *FAST,* TOO!
I'M COMIN', I'M COMIN'!

WOULD YOU LOOK AT *THAT!* THAT'S A STATE-OF-THE-ART REPLICA, RIGHT THERE.
AWW, THE LITTLE ROBOTS ARE SO *CUTE!*
ANDY REALLY WENT ALL OUT ON THIS ONE, DIDN'T HE?
WELL, IT *IS* A BIG IMPROVEMENT OVER LAST YEAR'S...I THINK THAT ONE WAS CALLED "COMPARE THE SIZES OF ROCKS."

I'VE GOT TO HAND IT TO THE KID. HE'S REALLY NAILED THE STANDARDIZATION HERE.
YOU COULD REALLY *BELIEVE* THIS THING WAS PUTTING TOGETHER ONE PRETEND CAR AFTER ANOTHER.

IT'S JUST SO COOL! LOOK AT ALL THE LITTLE PARTS AND, AND GIZMOS!

I GUESS IT'S OKAY... FOR WHAT IT IS...

OH? YOU THINK YOU COULD DO ANY BETTER, HAMM?
I'M JUST SAYING, I KNOW PLENTY ABOUT SCIENCE.

VALUABLE SCIENTIFIC FACTS--FACTS THAT COULD'VE HELPED ANDY.
WITH MY HELP? THIS THING COULD'VE BEEN GREAT.
NOT THAT ANYBODY ASKED FOR MY HELP...
GUYS!
I THINK ANDY'S COMING BACK!

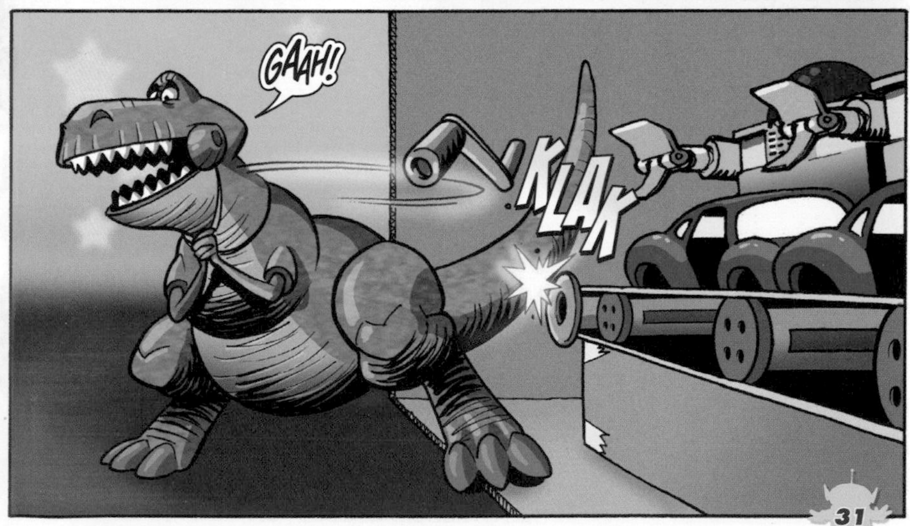
GAAH!
KLAK

AAAAHH!
I BROKE ANDY'S PROJECT!

I CAN'T BELIEVE I DID THAT! I CAN'T BELIEVE IT!
REX, IT'S GOING TO BE OKAY, BUT WE HAVE TO REPLACE THE CRANK AND GET BACK TO OUR PLACES!

HOW COULD I BE SO STUPID? HE WORKED SO HARD ON THIS! I CAN'T BELIEVE IT!
REX... COME ON...
HERE, I'LL PUT THE CRANK BACK ON. CAN YOU GET HIM DOWN OFF THE DRESSER, WOODY?

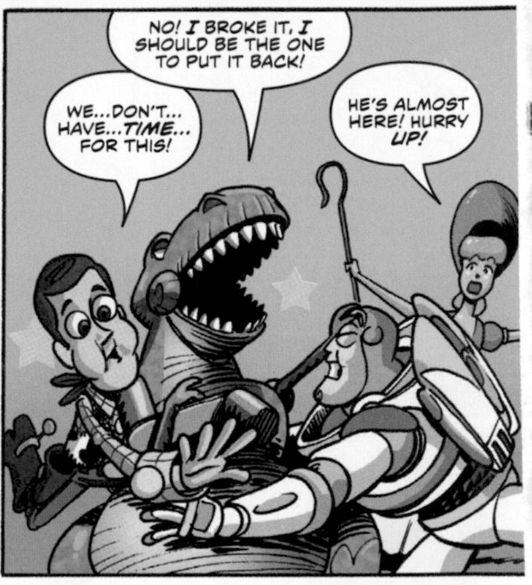
NO! I BROKE IT, I SHOULD BE THE ONE TO PUT IT BACK!
WE...DON'T... HAVE...TIME... FOR THIS!
HE'S ALMOST HERE! HURRY UP!

OKAY, SO WE GET THE THING SET UP TONIGHT, AND THE FAIR ITSELF STARTS WHEN?
TOMORROW MORNING AT NINE.

I GUESS THAT MAKES SENSE.
WELL THEN...

...ONE AUTOMOTIVE ASSEMBLY LINE, COMING UP!
BE CAREFUL!

IT'S GOT LOTS OF LITTLE PARTS!
RELAX, ALREADY!

LEAP
OH NO... OH NO OH NO OH NO!

ANDY'S PROJECT WON'T WORK NOW, BECAUSE OF ME!
WHAT'RE WE GONNA DO?
WELL, THE SITUATION COULD BE BETTER, I HAVE TO SAY.

IF ANDY LOSES THIS SCIENCE FAIR, IT'LL GO ON HIS PERMANENT RECORD!
I'VE HEARD ABOUT THOSE THINGS! IF THEY'RE NOT JUST RIGHT, YOU END UP MISERABLE FOR THE REST OF YOUR LIFE!
I CAN'T LET THAT HAPPEN! I JUST CAN'T!

AND YOU WON'T HAVE TO.
BECAUSE WE'RE GOING TO FIX THIS.

...HOW?
WE'RE GOING TO GO TO THIS SCIENCE FAIR. AND WE'RE GOING TO REPAIR ANDY'S PROJECT.
A SMALL STRIKE TEAM WOULD BE IDEAL. FOUR, MAYBE FIVE OF US. IT'LL BE A TACTICAL OPERATION.

NOT TO RAIN ON YOUR TACTICAL PARADE, BUZZ, BUT HOW ARE WE SUPPOSED TO GET THERE?
AND FOR THAT MATTER, DOES ANYBODY HERE EVEN KNOW WHERE THE PLACE IS?

I KNOW WHERE THE PLACE IS.
ANDY TOOK ME THERE LAST YEAR.
AND AS FOR HOW TO GET THERE...

"...I'VE GOT AN IDEA OR TWO."

OKAY! HE'S OUT!

WHY DO *I* HAVE TO GO, ANYWAY?

WE NEEDED SOMEBODY WHO'D BE ***SURE*** NOT TO LOSE THE ***CRANK,*** THAT'S WHY. WHAT'S MORE SECURE THAN A ***BANK?***

YEAH, WELL, IT'S RATTLING AROUND WITH ALL OF ANDY'S CHANGE AND MAKING ME QUEASY.

WAIT A MINUTE, THIS WAS YOUR IDEA? LASSO A CAR?
I'D HOLD ON TIGHT IF I WERE YOU, BO.

YIIIEEEEK!

DINOSAURS WEREN'T M-M-MEANT TO GO THIS FAST!
OH, PIPE DOWN! JUST ENJOY THE RIDE!

EASY FOR YOU TO SAY, B-B-BUZZ!
YOU DON'T HAVE A DOLLAR SIXTY-FIVE IN N-N-NICKELS JANGLING UP YOUR INSIDES!

WOO-HOOOO!

SKRAASH

EVERYONE OKAY? EVERYONE IN ONE PIECE?
YEAH-- *DESPITE* YOUR BEST EFFORTS...
WELL, FELLAS...

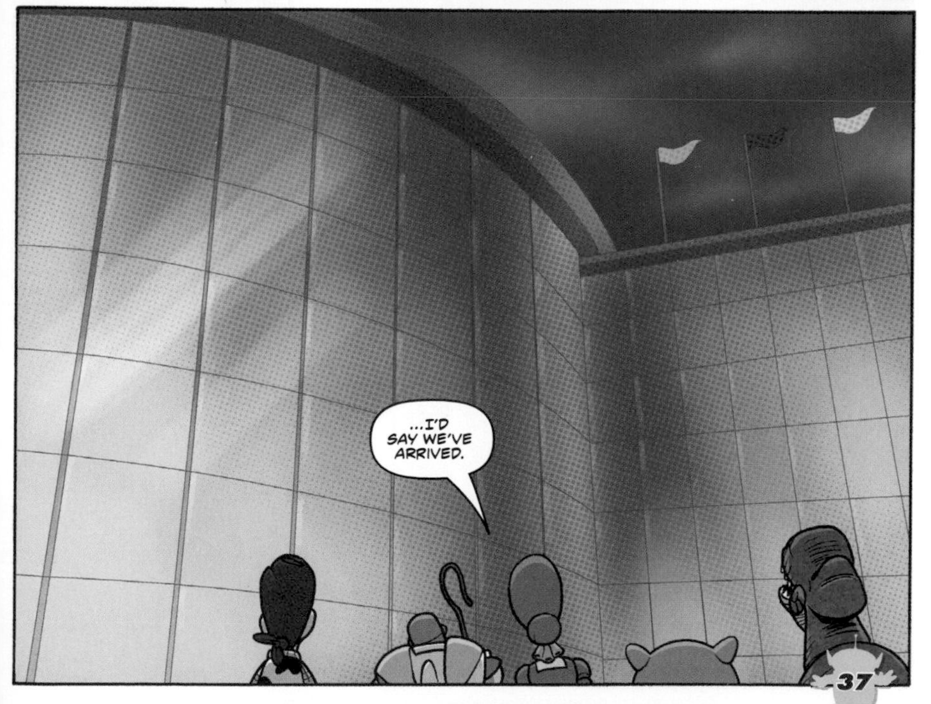
...I'D SAY WE'VE ARRIVED.

OKAY, WOODY, YOU GOT US HERE, I HAVE TO GIVE YOU THAT MUCH.
NOW HOW DO WE GET *INSIDE?*
WELL, I... UH...MY PLAN DIDN'T EXACTLY COVER...UM... BUZZ?
HEY, DON'T LOOK AT ME. I WAS STRICTLY THE *MOTIVATION* IN THIS ENDEAVOR.

WHAT IN THE WORLD?

SOME LITTLE RASCAL'S GOING TO BE AWFULLY GLAD TO SEE *YOU* GUYS COME TOMORROW, I'LL BET!
PROBABLY JUST FELL OUT OF THE FAMILY CAR, HUH?
WELL, I KNOW *RIGHT* WHERE TO TAKE YOU.

HERE YOU GO!
LOST
AND

I IMAGINE WHOEVER LOST YOU WILL COME AND GET YOU IN THE MORNING.

WELL... WE'RE INSIDE THE BUILDING NOW, HUH?

WE'VE BEEN A PART OF SOME SLOPPY PLANS IN THE PAST, BUT THIS TAKES THE CAKE.
YOU HAD NO CLUE HOW WE WERE GOING TO GET IN HERE, DID YOU?
I WAS GOING TO IMPROVISE! HAVEN'T YOU EVER IMPROVISED BEFORE?
GOSH, I HATE IT WHEN YOU TWO BICKER.

GUYS? HELLO-O?
IF WE'RE GOING TO FIX ANDY'S PROJECT, WE DO HAVE TO FIND IT.

THE WATCHMAN'S GONE--GOOD. OKAY.
LET'S HEAD FOR THOSE BIG DOORS.

BO? CAN YOU SEE ANYTHING?
...BO?
OH, I CAN SEE SOMETHING, ALL RIGHT.

IT'S CALLED A "JACKPOT."
EMPLOYEES ONLY
BEANS AND THE HUMAN RESPONSE
P-U!
CAN FISH READ YOUR MIND?
Can Crickets learn to Tap Dance?
DOES RAISING ALLOWANCE IMPROVE BEHAVIOR?

HRRGH... *PUSH!*
I'M PUSHING!
The effects of ice cream on embedded circuits
by Billy Mitchell
OKAY. ANDY'S PROJECT HAS TO BE IN HERE SOMEWHERE.
ALL WE HAVE TO DO IS *FIND* IT.
THANK YOU, CAPTAIN OBVIOUS OF STAR COMMAND.

"CAN FISH READ YOUR MIND?" ...NOPE, THAT'S NOT IT.
"TEN COMMON HOUSEHOLD PRODUCTS THAT CAN BE USED TO BUILD AN INDUSTRIAL LASER." HUH.

"FORTY-THREE USES FOR DRYER LINT?"
I *KNOW* I COULD COME UP WITH A BETTER PROJECT THAN *THAT.*

THERE IT IS! *THERE IT IS!*

OKAY. THERE'S ANDY'S PROJECT.
HAMM? GOT THE CRANK?
I'VE GOT IT, I'VE GOT IT. LET'S JUST GET UP THERE.

YOU OKAY, REX?
YEAH, I JUST...IF I CAN GRAB THE CLOTH WITH MY *TEETH...*
HRGH...WOULD *STAIRS* HAVE BEEN TOO MUCH TO ASK FOR?

OKAY, HAMM, YOU'RE UP.
DAVE 5000
ARTIFICIALLY INTELLIGENT
ROBOTIC ACTION
ON/OFF

HAMM?
KLICK

HI, FRIEND! WHAT'S YOUR NAME?
HUH HUH HAMM...!
HI THERE, "HUH HUH HAMM!" WHERE DO YOU GO TO SCHOOL?
GO TO SCHOOL? I DON'T GO TO SCHOOL!

WOW, THAT'S NEAT! I BET "GO TO SCHOOL? I DON'T GO TO SCHOOL!" IS A GREAT PLACE!
WHAT'S YOUR FAVORITE FOOD, "HUH HUH HAMM?"
MY FAV--
LUG NUTS AND SPIDERS.

AWESOME! I LIKE "LUG NUTS AND SPIDERS" TOO!
DO YOU--
KLICK

DID YOU ALL SEE THIS--THIS THING OVER HERE? THIS IS JUST WRONG!

ALL DAY LONG, I SIT AROUND, NOT ALLOWED TO TALK, NOOOO, I HAVE TO BE A GOOD TOY AND KEEP MY MOUTH SHUT!
COME ON, HAMM. THIS ISN'T THE TIME.

NO, OF COURSE NOT! IT'S NEVER THE TIME, IS IT?
WE NEVER GET TO TALK, OR LET ANYBODY KNOW WHO WE REALLY ARE, AND WHAT HAPPENS?
THEY BUILD THIS DAVE THING THAT JUST PARROTS WHAT PEOPLE SAY TO IT--IN THE DUMBEST POSSIBLE WAY, I MIGHT ADD.

I'LL STAND UP THERE AND TALK! HOW ABOUT THAT?
I'LL SHOUT AT SOME KID WALKING BY, AND SAY "HEY, YOU, IN THE WHITE SHIRT AND BLUE HAT! HOW'S IT GOING?"
IT WON'T BE ARTIFICIAL THEN, WILL IT? THEY WON'T HAVE TO BUILD ALL THIS RIDICULOUS, FAKE...RIDICULOUS STUFF!

I KNOW IT'S NOT FAIR, HAMM, BUT WE REALLY NEED TO THINK ABOUT ANDY NOW.
LET'S GET THAT CRANK BACK IN PLACE, HUH? WHADDAYA SAY, THERE, PARTNER?

OH, RIGHT--
ANDY...AND THE
CRANK. UM.
YEAH, I...
I GUESS WE
SHOULD DO
THAT, HUH?
ATTABOY!

HELLO?

IS SOMEBODY
DOWN THERE?

HEY!

IS THAT--
WAS THAT
KIDS?

HOW DID KIDS GET IN HERE IN THE MIDDLE OF THE NIGHT?

WHA--?
NOW THEY'RE RUNNING RADIO-CONTROLLED TOYS AROUND?

WHAT THE--
VOLCANOS

HOW MANY OF YOU ARE THERE?

NOW YOU LISTEN TO ME, I *WILL* CALL YOUR PARENTS IF I HAVE T--

THIPP

THAT'S NOT FUNNY!

WHO DID THAT?

WHERE ARE YOU?

DON'T YOU RUN FROM ME, YOUNGSTER!
many marbles
this jar?

WHAA-HAA-HAAAAH!
BABY BROTHERS: BLESSING OR MENACE?
How many marbles are in this jar?

FOG BANKS + YOU: THE VAP RIZING EFFECTS F DRY
CLIK
FSSSHHHH

I'LL FIND YOU! JUST BECAUSE I CAN'T *SEE* YOU...

...DOESN'T MEAN I WON'T...
...*FIND* YOU...

HUH?

HI THERE! I'M DAVE! WHAT'S *YOUR* NAME?
...PETE...?
HI THERE, "PETE!" I CAN TALK! JUST LIKE A REAL PERSON! WHERE'D YOU GROW UP, PETE?
ON/OFF

UH... CINCINNATI.
WHAT'S GOING ON HERE?
THAT'S GREAT! I'M SURE "CINCINNATI WHAT'S GOING ON HERE" IS A *GREAT* PLACE!
WHAT SCHOOL DO YOU GO TO, PETE?

OH...YOU'RE SAYING WHAT I'M SAYING, HUH?
AWESOME! I BET "OH YOU'RE SAYING WHAT I'M SAYING" IS A *GREAT* SCHOOL!

ƐCLICK BEEEPƐ HI THERE, "THE WATCHMAN'S COMING WE HAVE TO GO!"
I'LL BET "HEAD FOR THE MAIN ENTRANCE THE BIKES ARE IN THE PARKING LOT" IS A *GREAT* SCHOOL!

BIKES IN THE PARKING LOT, HUH?

WE'LL *SEE* WHO GETS AWAY AND WHO DOESN'T!

IS HE GONE? I THINK HE'S GONE!
ON/OF

OH, HAMM, I'VE GOT TO SAY *BRA-VO!* THAT WAS *BRILLIANT!*
BUZZ IS RIGHT, THAT WAS *PERFECT!*
HOW'D YOU *THINK* OF THAT?

WELL, THAT'S WHAT PEOPLE EXPECT FROM TOYS THAT CAN "TALK," ISN'T IT?
JUST A DUMB HUNK OF JUNK THAT SPITS BACK OUT WHAT YOU GIVE IT.

YEAH, BUT--DON'T YOU SEE? IF PEOPLE DIDN'T EXPECT THAT, THERE'S NO WAY YOU COULD'VE PULLED THIS OFF!
YOU'VE SAVED THE DAY, HAMM!
YEAH! YOU'RE A HERO!

MAYBE SO. BUT IT'S STILL NOT FAIR.
OH, COME ON. LET'S SAY YOU COULD TALK TO PEOPLE OPENLY. WHAT WOULD YOU SAY THAT'S SO IMPORTANT?
ARE YOU SERIOUS? I'D SHARE MY KNOWLEDGE WITH THEM!

THAT'S IT? YOU'D JUST... TELL THEM STUFF?
HEY, I'M A STOREHOUSE OF FACTS! VALUABLE FACTS!
BUT STILL--YOU'D RISK EVERYTHING, JUST TO...PROVE HOW MUCH STUFF YOU'VE MEMORIZED?
YOU PEOPLE DON'T KNOW ME AT ALL!
THE END

HOWDY
PARDNER

Chapter 3

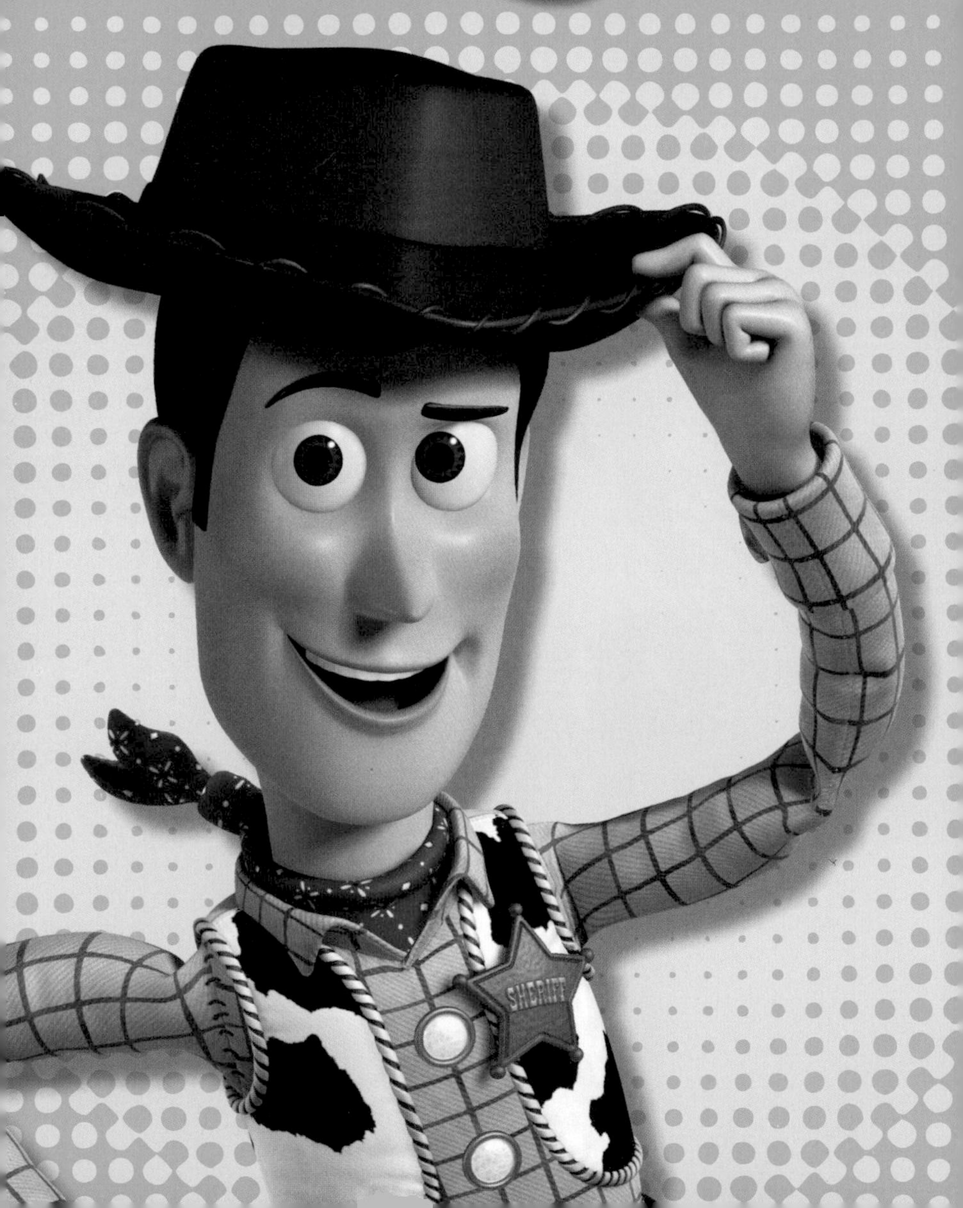

AAHHCHOO!

BUSTER! SLOW DOWN!

SNIFF

BUSTER...

...COME BACK HERE!

BUSTER, YOU LIKE BEING BRUSHED! WHAT'S YOUR PROBLEM?

I THINK HE'S CUTE!
YEAH. IT'S SORT OF LIKE HAVING A BIG, HYPER OLDER BROTHER. KIND OF.

WELL.
I, FOR ONE, AM *APPALLED*.
AH, C'MON, BO. HE'S NOT *THAT* BAD.

I'M SORRY, GUYS--I HATE TO BE ALL NEGATIVE NANCY HERE--BUT DON'T YOU THINK WE SHOULD BE A *LITTLE* WORRIED?
BUSTER IS A *REAL* DOG!
IF ANDY HAS A REAL DOG...AND I MEAN NO OFFENSE BY THIS, SLINK...BUT WHY WOULD HE WANT TO PLAY WITH A TOY DOG?
OH...OH DEAR...I HADN'T THOUGHT ABOUT IT LIKE THAT...
THERE'S POTENTIAL FOR IT TO GET WORSE, TOO.
YOU KNOW WHO CAN MOVE ON HIS *OWN? BUSTER.* YOU KNOW WHO CAN MAKE *NOISE* ON HIS OWN? *BUSTER!*
HE'S SUPERIOR TO US IN EVERY WAY!
I *KNEW* DOGS WERE MORE POPULAR THAN DINOSAURS! I *KNEW* IT!
NOOO! WHAT IF THIS STARTS A *TREND?* WHAT IF HE GETS A *REAL PIG,* TOO?

UH OH.
DAMAGE CONTROL.

WHAT IF ANDY DECIDES HE DOESN'T LIKE TOY *SHEEP?*
WHAT IF HE WANTS TO GET RID OF *MINE?*

MA'AM! WE WILL SAFEGUARD THE WELL-BEING OF YOUR SHEEP FROM THAT FOUL CREATURE! MA'AM!

PUPPIES DROOL, DON'T THEY? I COULD DROOL!
AND I COULD BE MORE PIG-LIKE! COULDN'T I? LET'S MAKE A MUD PUDDLE!
I ALWAYS THOUGHT IT WAS A *GOOD* THING THAT I DIDN'T SHED...WHAT IF ANDY *LIKES* DOG HAIR?

I THINK IT'S YOUR TURN.
NO PROBLEM.

EVERYONE...
EVERYONE!
LISTEN TO ME, PLEASE!

YOU ALL NEED TO CALM DOWN. YOU'RE GETTING EXCITED OVER NOTHING!
A PUPPY AND A TOY ARE TWO COMPLETELY DIFFERENT THINGS!
JUST BECAUSE ANDY HAS A DOG NOW, DOESN'T MEAN HE'S GOING TO BE ANY LESS INTERESTED IN US!

UM...NOT MEANING ANY DISRESPECT, BUZZ, BUT...DO YOU HAVE ANY EVIDENCE TO SUPPORT THAT?
YEAH! HAVE YOU EVER LIVED IN A HOUSE WITH A DOG BEFORE?

WELL, NO, BUT IT'S SELF-EVIDENT.
DOES ANDY HAVE TO WALK US? NO! DOES ANDY HAVE TO TAKE US TO THE VET? NO!
IT'S JUST TWO COMPLETELY DIF-

THAT'S NICE AND ALL, BUZZ--
--BUT WE'VE GOTTA FIGURE OUT WHAT TO DO!
I SAY WE PANIC!

OUCH. SHUT DOWN.
EH. YOU WIN SOME, YOU LOSE SOME.
WHOA. GUYS.

WAS IT MY POSTURE? SHOULD I HAVE GONE MORE HEROIC?
GUYS!
HUH?
WHAT IS IT?

OH.

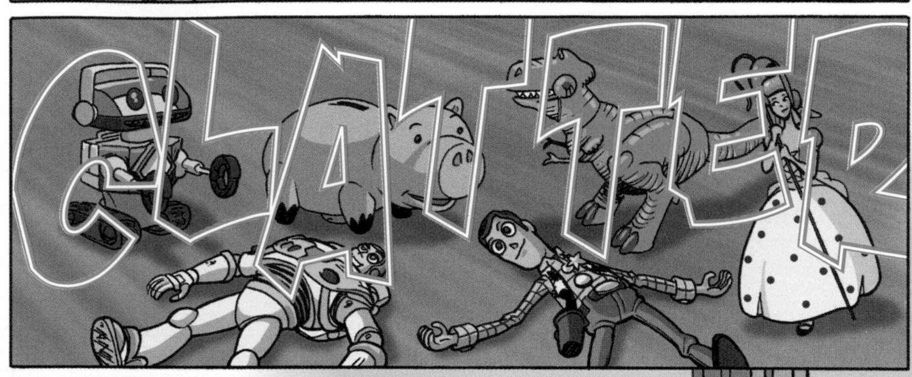
CLATTER

IS THE DOG BUYING IT?
I DON'T THINK SO.

BUSTER! THERE YOU ARE!
C'MON, BOY! IT'S *FOOD* TIME.
YOU WANT SOME PUPPY CHOW, DON'TCHA?

WHAT'RE WE GOING TO DO?
I DON'T KNOW...

"...BUT I'VE GOT THE FEELING IT'S GOING TO GET WORSE BEFORE IT GETS BETTER."
YOU WANT THE BALL, BOY? YOU WANT THE BALL?

GO GET IT! GO GET THE BALL!

WHAT--
BUSTER! WHERE DID YOU GET BUZZ?

WHAT'RE YOU TRYING TO DO, BOY?
WHINE... WHI-I-INE

BUZZ LIGHTYEAR IS NOT SOMETHING YOU FETCH. OKAY?

WE'LL JUST PUT HIM BACK IN HERE.
ANDY

NO MORE FETCHING BUZZ. GOT THAT?

AFTER ANDY AND BUSTER LEAVE...
ARE YOU OKAY, BUZZ?
THAT MUST HAVE BEEN TERRIFYING!
OUR WORST SUSPICIONS ARE CONFIRMED, PEOPLE. THAT DOG IS ACTIVELY TRYING TO BLOW THE WHISTLE ON US.
PLUS I'M COVERED IN DOG SPIT. WHO'S GOT A TOWELETTE?

MOMENTS LATER...
HOLD TOTALLY STILL! THE T-REX'S VISION IS BASED ON MOVEMENT!
I'LL SAVE YOU, SLINKY DOG!
STAR COMMAND HAS A STRICT NO-DOGS-EATEN-BY-DINOSAURS POLICY!

TO INFINITY, AND--

BARK!
HEY!

WHAT'S GOTTEN INTO YOU, BOY?
WHY'RE YOU ACTING SO WEIRD AROUND MY TOYS?
RRHOWF!

YOU ALL RIGHT, REX?
I THINK SOME OF MY SMALL PARTS CAME LOOSE!

HE'S NOT GIVING UP, IS HE?
DOESN'T LOOK LIKE IT.
GOT A PLAN YET?
NO...
FWIP

"...BUT I'LL LET YOU KNOW AS SOON AS I DO."
AAACHOO!

WHY CAN'T I STAY HOME FROM SCHOOL WHEN I FEEL GOOD?
THIS STINKS.
BARK!
HEY, BUSTER! WHAT'S--
HEY!
WHAT ARE YOU DOING?

BUSTER, NO!

DON'T!

OOF!
PLOP

NOW LOOK, YOU. I'M NOT GOING TO LOCK YOU OUT OF MY ROOM.
YOU'RE JUST GOING TO HAVE TO LEARN TO GET ALONG WITH MY TOYS.

YOU GOT THAT?
...YOU'RE NOT HEARING A WORD I'M SAYING, ARE YOU?
WOW, BO DIDN'T EVEN MAKE A *SOUND*. I'M IMPRESSED.
SHE'S ONE TOUGH SHEPHERDESS, IT'S TRUE.
HEY! LOOK AT THAT!

OH! DO YOU NEED TO GO OUT? IS THAT WHY YOU WEREN'T LISTENING?

ALL RIGHT, ALL RIGHT, YOU CAN GO OUT.

BUT WE'RE HAVING A *TALK* WHEN YOU COME BACK IN, MISTER.
LOOKS LIKE *SOME*BODY HAD A FULL BLADDER.
YEAH!

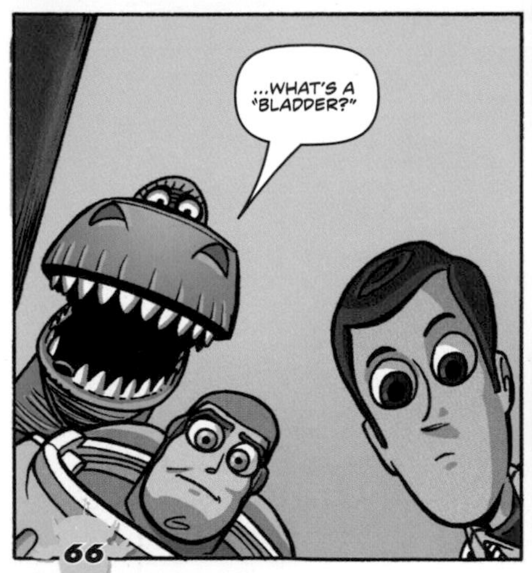
...WHAT'S A "BLADDER?"

COME ON. LET'S HEAD BACK TO ANDY'S ROOM.

C'MON...
THIS WAY.
PSST.
HEY!

HEY
BUSTER!
BUSTER!

RRHN?

C'MERE! WE'VE
GOT SOMETHING
FOR YOU!
C'MERE!
COME GET
IT!

YEAH--LOOK AT THAT. THAT'S A NICE DOGGIE TREAT, ISN'T IT?
WELL, IT CAN BE YOURS...
...IF YOU MAKE A DEAL WITH US.

YOU KNOW WE CAN MOVE AND TALK ON OUR OWN. AND WE KNOW HOW SMART YOU ARE.
IT'S IMPORTANT TO US THAT NOBODY KNOWS ABOUT THESE THINGS WE CAN DO.

SO HERE. PLEASE ACCEPT THIS...AS A PEACE OFFERING. WE DON'T WANT ANY TROUBLE WITH YOU.
AND WE'RE HOPING YOU WON'T KEEP LOOKING FOR ANY WITH US.

BARK!

THAT'S ONE STUBBORN DOG.
GOT A PLAN B? 'CAUSE I'D LOVE TO HEAR IT.

YEAH, WE WOULD TOO!
WHAT'RE WE GONNA *DO?* HE'LL *EXPOSE* US!

REX IS RIGHT, YOU KNOW.
IT'S ONLY A MATTER OF TIME BEFORE BUSTER *SURPRISES* ONE OF US, AND IT'S ALL OVER.

I HATE EVEN TO SUGGEST THIS, BUT...
...MAYBE WE SHOULD CONSIDER... *RELOCATING* BUSTER?

YES! *YES!* WHAT A GREAT IDEA!
WELL... IT *WOULD* SOLVE ALL OUR PROBLEMS...

WHOA, WHOA, WHOA, PEOPLE, C'MON, WOULD YOU LISTEN TO YOURSELVES?

WE CAN'T GET RID OF BUSTER! YOU KNOW HOW MUCH ANDY LOVES HIM!
BUT HE'S GONNA PROVE WE CAN WALK AND TALK ON OUR OWN! WHAT THEN? WHAT THEN?
LOOK, YOU'RE MISSING THE BIGGER PICTURE HERE.
BUSTER IS A DOG--A REAL, LIVE, FLESH-AND-BLOOD DOG.

AND THAT DOG...IS GOING TO GROW UP. FAST.
HE'LL ONLY BE A PUPPY FOR SO LONG, AND THEN HE'LL BE A GROWN-UP DOG FOR SO LONG, AND THEN... THAT'S IT.
WE, ON THE OTHER HAND, ARE TIME-LESS!

I MEAN, COME ON, LOOK AT ME! I'VE BEEN AROUND FOR DECADES, I'M NONE THE WORSE FOR WEAR, AND ANDY LOVES ME TO PIECES.
HE'LL ALWAYS HAVE US. BUZZ WAS RIGHT BEFORE.

YOU JUST CAN'T COMPARE A PET WITH A GOOD, SOLID, OLD-FASHIONED TOY!

GOOD JOB--YOU GOT THROUGH TO THEM.
THANKS.
ANY IDEA WHAT WE'RE GOING TO DO ABOUT BUSTER?
NOT A CLUE.

SKRITCH
SKRITCH
SKRITCH

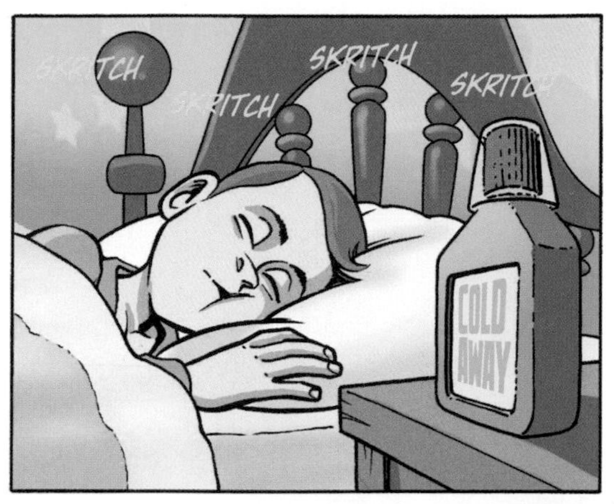
SKRITCH
SKRITCH
SKRITCH
COLD AWAY

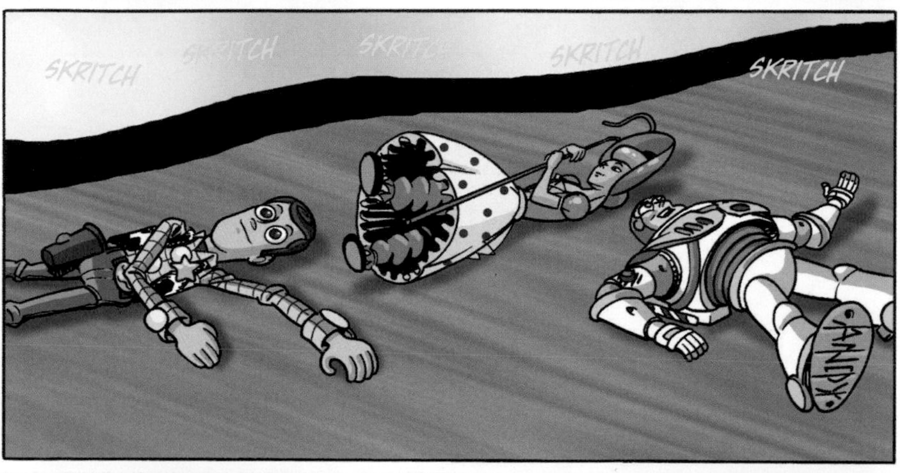
SKRITCH
SKRITCH
SKRITCH
SKRITCH
SKRITCH
ANDY

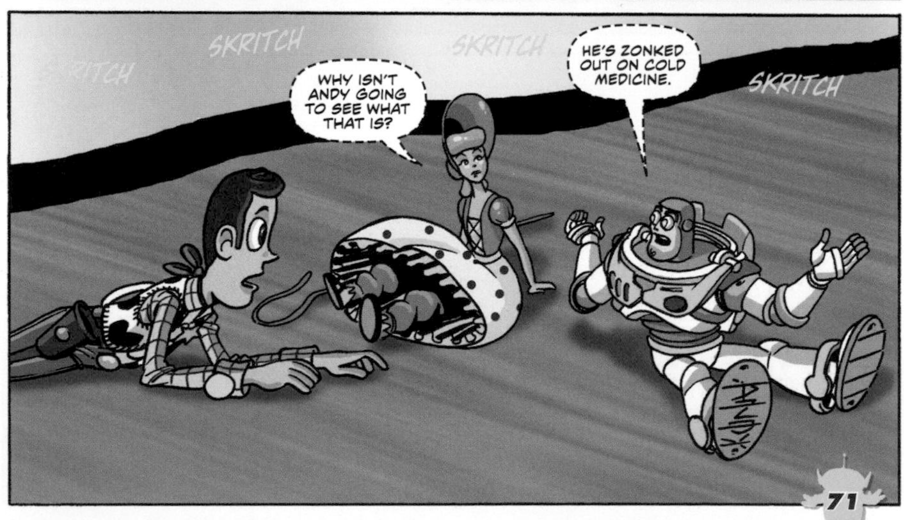
SKRITCH
SKRITCH
SKRITCH
SKRITCH
WHY ISN'T ANDY GOING TO SEE WHAT THAT IS?
HE'S ZONKED OUT ON COLD MEDICINE.
ANDY

"AH HA. THE FULL BLADDER STRIKES AGAIN."
HE'S NOT GOING TO WIND UP GOING ON THE *CARPET,* IS HE?
NAH...ANDY'S MOM WILL HEAR HIM EVENTUALLY. I'M SURE SHE'LL COME AND LET HIM OUT.
HMMM...
GUYS, JUST WAIT HERE, OKAY?

WOODY! WHAT'RE YOU *DOING?*

RELAX.
I THINK I'VE GOT AN IDEA.

HEY THERE, BUSTER.
YOU REALLY WANT TO GO OUT, DON'T YOU?

NORMALLY ANDY LETS YOU OUT, HUH? BUT ANDY CAN'T HEAR YOU RIGHT NOW.
IT'S JUST YOU AND ME...AND A KING-SIZED CALL OF NATURE, HUH?

WELL, LISTEN UP. BECAUSE WE CAN HELP EACH OTHER.
YOU AGREE TO KEEP OUR, AH, TALENTS TO YOURSELF--AND STOP TRYING TO EXPOSE US...
...AND I'LL OPEN THAT DOOR FOR YOU.

WHAT DO YOU SAY?
GRRRRRHHH...

WHUFF.
FANTASTIC!

OKAY, I'LL NEED A BOOST.

ALL RIGHT...THAT'S GOOD...HERE WE GO...

MINUTES LATER...
OH, LOOK! BUSTER'S FINALLY COMING BACK IN!
TOOK 'EM LONG ENOUGH.
ANDY

EVERYONE, I'D LIKE TO INTRODUCE YOU FORMALLY TO *BUSTER*.
BUSTER IS A *NEW FRIEND*...
...AND I THINK WE'RE GOING TO GET ALONG JUST *FINE* NOW.
THE END

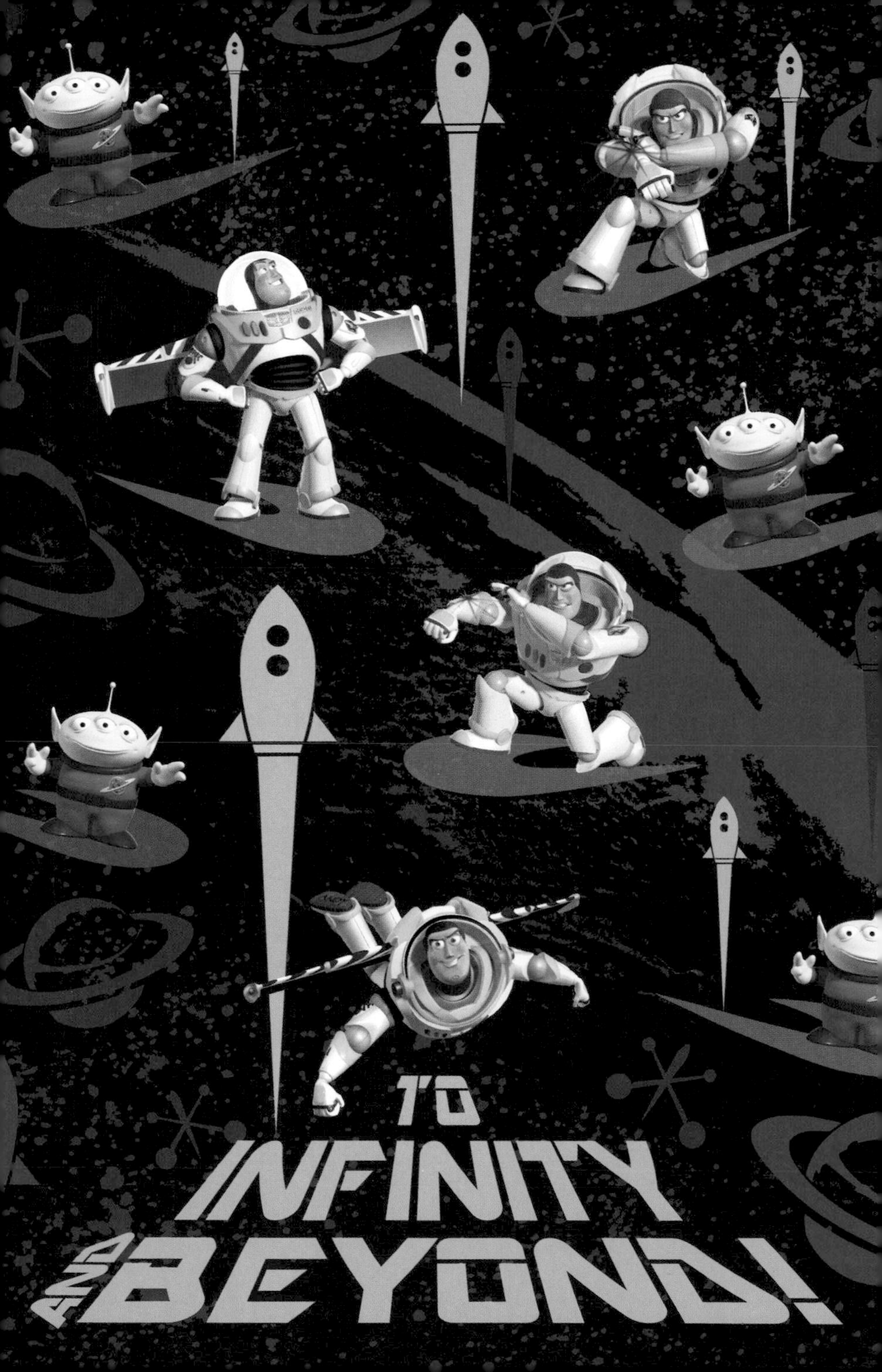
TO
INFINITY
AND
BEYOND!

Chapter 4

EVACUATE!
EVERYBODY EVACUATE!
THE MONSTER CAN'T BE STOPPED!
GET OUT OF HIS WAY!
OR HE'LL SQUISH YOU LIKE A PANCAKE!
IT'S UP TO US, MEN! THE SUPER-ANTI-MONSTER BATTALION!
WE JUST HAVE TO HOPE DR. CLOCKWORK'S INVENTION DOES THE JOB!
PRIVATE JENSEN! IS THE MONSTER-BUSTER ROCKET READY TO FIRE?

ANDY! TIME FOR SCHOOL!
DON'T MAKE ME TELL YOU AGAIN!
ALL RIGHT, ALL RIGHT...
...I'M ON MY WAY!
BONK
OW!

I COULDN'T FIND MY GOOD SOCKS...
DID YOU LOOK IN YOUR SOCK DRAWER, LIKE I ASKED YOU TO?
OH HEY! THERE THEY ARE!

YOU'RE REALLY GOOD AT THAT, MOM!

YEAH, IT TAKES A LOT OF SKILL TO LOOK FOR SOCKS IN A SOCK DRAWER.

ARE THEY GONE?
I THINK SO. LOOK, SARGE --
IT'S OKAY ...SIR.
THIS ISN'T THE FIRST TIME A MEMBER OF THIS COMPANY'S GOTTEN SEPARATED.
WE ALL HAVE FOND MEMORIES OF CORPORAL THOMAS, BEFORE THAT UNFORTUNATE LAWNMOWER INCIDENT.
I JUST HAVE TO TRUST THAT ANDY WILL BRING JENSEN BACK.

UHM...FELLAS? I DON'T MEAN TO BE AN ALARMIST, BUT...
DIDN'T ANDY SAY, LAST TIME HE TOOK ANY OF THE ARMY GUYS TO SCHOOL, THAT BOBBY HATHAWAY WAS REALLY JEALOUS?
AND THAT NEXT TIME, HE WAS AFRAID BOBBY MIGHT TRY TO SWIPE SOME OF THEM?

SWIPE? SWIPE?
WELL THAT IS JUST FANTASTIC! I'VE GOT ANOTHER MAN OUT IN THE COLD, AND NOW IT'S LIKELY HE WON'T EVER MAKE IT BACK!

SARGE, JENSEN'S A GOOD SOLDIER...HE KNOWS THE RISKS INVOLVED IN--
SORRY, COMMANDER. THIS IS AN ARMY THING. I DON'T THINK YOU'D UNDERSTAND.

AND IT'S TIME TO TREAT THIS LIKE AN ARMY THING.

MEN! IT'S TIME TO GET JENSEN BACK!
WE'RE GONNA DO THIS OUR WAY --
CLEAN.
EFFICIENT.
NO WASTED EFFORT!

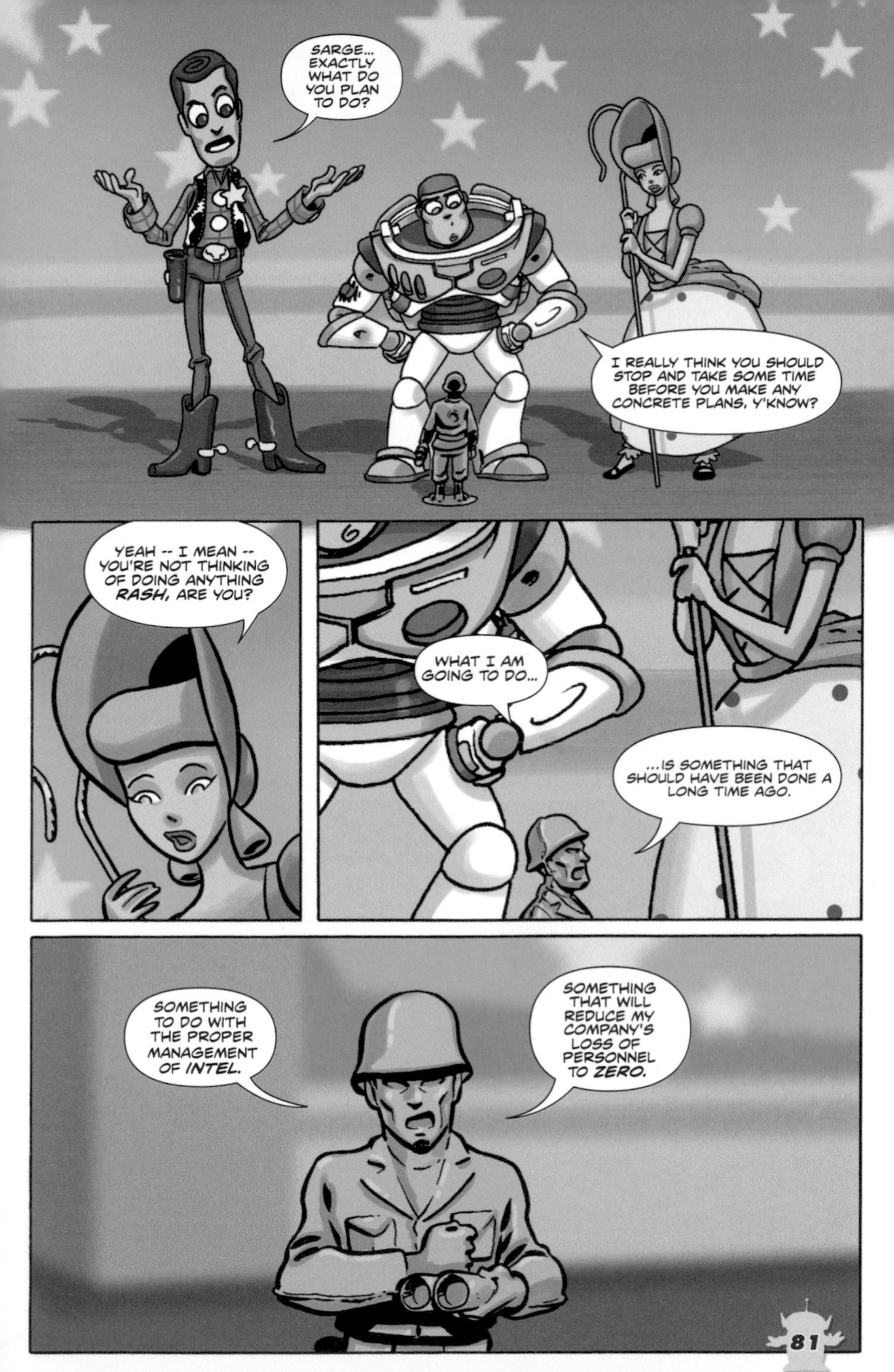
SARGE... EXACTLY WHAT DO YOU PLAN TO DO?
I REALLY THINK YOU SHOULD STOP AND TAKE SOME TIME BEFORE YOU MAKE ANY CONCRETE PLANS, Y'KNOW?
YEAH -- I MEAN -- YOU'RE NOT THINKING OF DOING ANYTHING *RASH*, ARE YOU?
WHAT I AM GOING TO DO...
...IS SOMETHING THAT SHOULD HAVE BEEN DONE A LONG TIME AGO.
SOMETHING TO DO WITH THE PROPER MANAGEMENT OF *INTEL*.
SOMETHING THAT WILL REDUCE MY COMPANY'S LOSS OF PERSONNEL TO *ZERO*.

I AM GOING TO INFORM ANDY OF OUR ABILITY TO TALK.
THAT WAY HE WON'T EVER MISPLACE ANY OF US AGAIN.

SARGE, YOU CAN'T BE SERIOUS--!
BUT THAT'S NOT HOW WE DO THINGS!
SARGE, SARGE, HOLD ON!

WE ARE GOING TO LET THE BOY ANDY KNOW EXACTLY WHAT HE'S DEALING WITH!
YES, SERGEANT!
WE ARE GOING TO PREVENT ANY FURTHER LOSS OF MANPOWER DUE TO HIS IGNORANCE OF THE SITUATION!
YES, SERGEANT!

WHO ELSE IS WITH ME? WHO ELSE WANTS THEIR VOICES HEARD?
YOU, PUCK? YOU, ROCKY?
MAYBE EVEN YOU, SLINKY. YOU DON'T TALK MUCH.
WELL, NOW...

I THINK HE'S SERIOUS.
I THINK YOU'RE RIGHT. THIS IS BAD....

I KNEW YOU GUYS WOULD SEE THINGS MY WAY!
NOW...

TO THE WINDOW!

GO
GO
GO
GO!

THAT'S IT --

OBJECTIVE ACHIEVED!

NOW -- TO THE SCHOOL!

SORRY, SARGE.

WHAP

CAN'T LET YOU DO IT.
SHUNK

GOOD JOB, SLINK!
'TWEREN'T NOTHIN'.

PLAN B!
ON THE OFFENSIVE!

MOVE OUT!

YES, SERGEANT!

HEY! HEY!
WHAP
FWUMP
NOW THIS IS UNCALLED FOR!

SARGE ISN'T THE ONLY ONE WITH *PLANS!*
REX! HAMM! OPERATION FLOOR-SWEEPER!

OOOH!
OOOOH! WE'VE GOT *ORDERS!*
JUST DON'T MESS 'EM UP, THERE, LIZARD-LIPS!

PULL!
PULLING!
MEDIC!

OUT*STANDING* PLANNING, BUZZ!
THAT DID WORK PRETTY WELL, IF I DO SAY SO MYSELF!
UH... GUYS... BEFORE YOU START BUMPING CHESTS...

YOUR GREAT PLAN HIT EVERYTHING BUT THE BULL'S EYE.

OOOOH NO, YOU DON'T!

CAN'T LET YOU DO THIS...

...YOU LITTLE GREEN *WEIRDO!*
ANDY

WHERE'D YOU GO?
WHERE'D YOU GO?

SHOOKA

WOODY?
WHERE ARE THEY?
THE CHIMNEY!

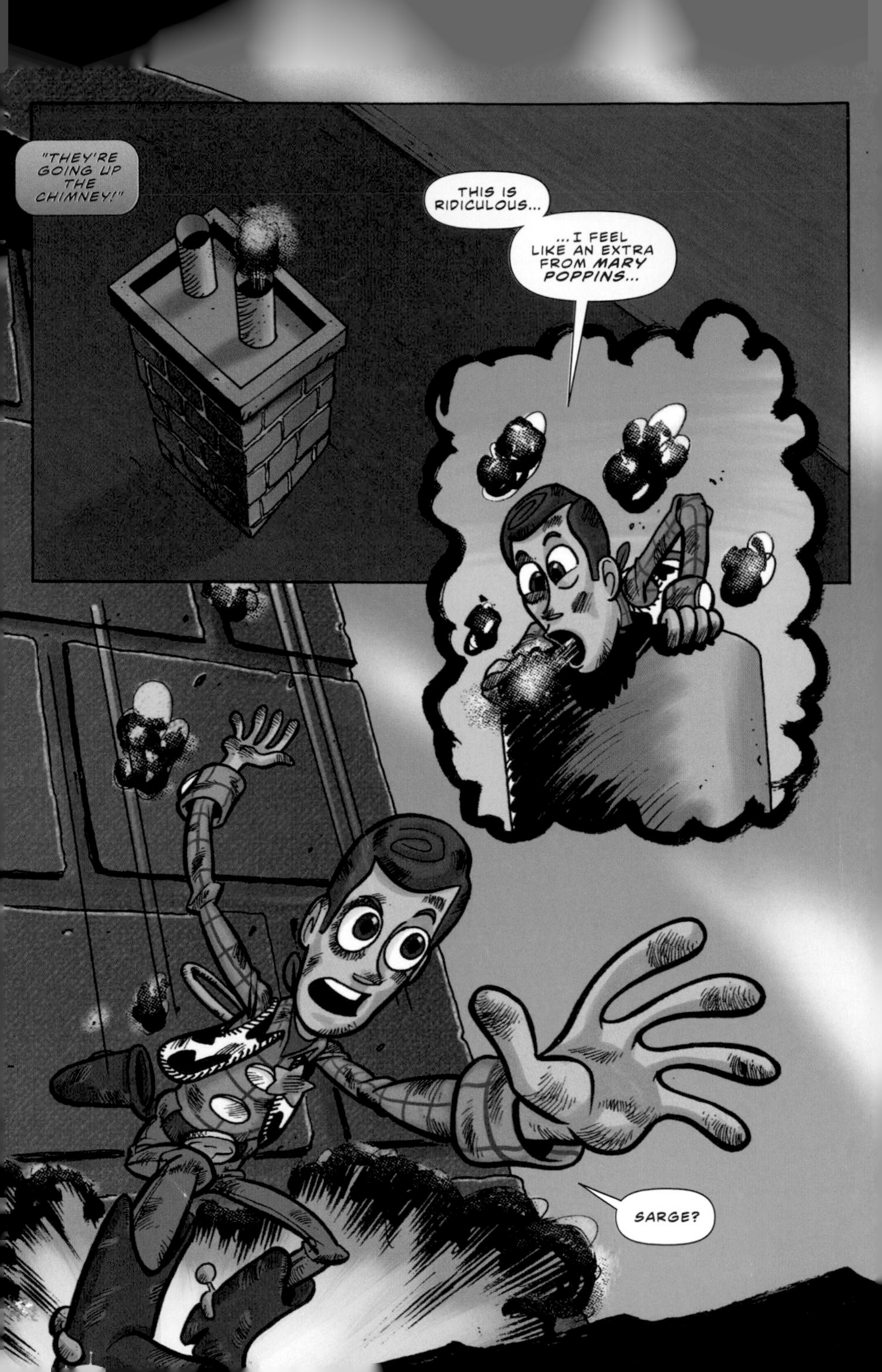
"THEY'RE GOING UP THE CHIMNEY!"
THIS IS RIDICULOUS...
...I FEEL LIKE AN EXTRA FROM MARY POPPINS...
SARGE?

SARGE!

I'M JUST SAYING, WE COULD USE SOME PARACHUTES.
I MEAN, I *HAVE* ONE. IT'S CAMO-PATTERN AND EVERYTHING.
LOOK, THORPE...
...YOU WEIGH ABOUT *HALF AN OUNCE* SOAKING WET.

YOU'LL BE LUCKY IF A *STIFF BREEZE* DOESN'T CARRY YOU OFF!
NOW I *SAID JUMP,* AND I *MEANT* IT!

SAAAARGE!

SARGE... SARGE, LISTEN TO ME... PLEASE.
I'M SORRY, SIR, BUT YOU'RE NOT GOING TO CHANGE MY MIND. I NEED TO DO THIS.

YOU'RE MISTAKEN, SARGE. AND I CAN TELL YOU WHY.
CAN I HAVE ONE MINUTE? WILL YOU AND YOUR SOLDIERS GIVE ME THAT?

LOOK...RIGHT NOW...YOU GUYS ARE AN ARMY. AND YOU CAN BE ANY KIND OF ARMY.
YOU KNOW? I MEAN...

...JUST TODAY, YOU WERE THE SUPER-ANTI-MONSTER-BATTALION. RIGHT?
LAST WEEK YOU WERE THE GREEN SCOURGE OF PLANET ZORMAX...
...AND THE WEEK BEFORE THAT, YOU YOURSELF, SARGE, WERE GENERAL GROMDAR OF THE JUPITER LEGION.

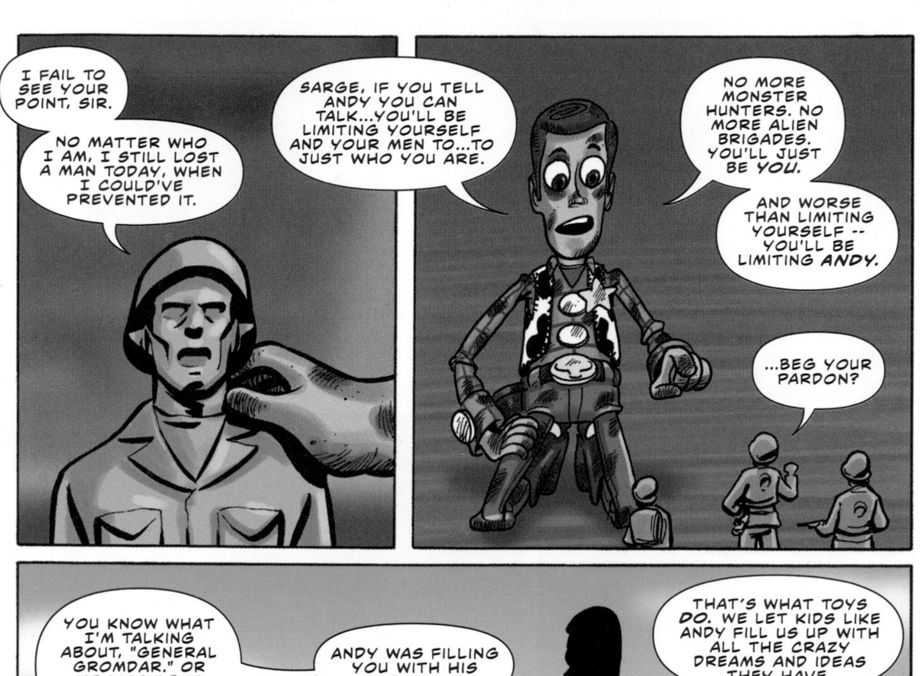
I FAIL TO SEE YOUR POINT, SIR.
NO MATTER WHO I AM, I STILL LOST A MAN TODAY, WHEN I COULD'VE PREVENTED IT.
SARGE, IF YOU TELL ANDY YOU CAN TALK...YOU'LL BE LIMITING YOURSELF AND YOUR MEN TO...TO JUST WHO YOU ARE.
NO MORE MONSTER HUNTERS. NO MORE ALIEN BRIGADES. YOU'LL JUST BE *YOU.*
AND WORSE THAN LIMITING YOURSELF -- YOU'LL BE LIMITING *ANDY.*
...BEG YOUR PARDON?

YOU KNOW WHAT I'M TALKING ABOUT, "GENERAL GROMDAR." OR YOU WOULD IF YOU STOPPED TO THINK A MINUTE.
ANDY WAS FILLING YOU WITH HIS IMAGINATION.
THAT'S WHAT TOYS *DO.* WE LET KIDS LIKE ANDY FILL US UP WITH ALL THE CRAZY DREAMS AND IDEAS THEY HAVE.
KIDS *NEED* TOYS.

IF YOU START *TALKING* TO HIM, THEN YOU'LL STOP BEING A TOY. YOU'LL BECOME A *FRIEND.*
AND ANDY *HAS* FRIENDS... OTHER LITTLE *BOYS AND GIRLS.*
I THINK YOU KNOW I'M RIGHT ABOUT THIS. DEEP DOWN.

THERE'S NO WAY A FRIEND IS GOING TO BE GENERAL GROMDAR, IS THERE?
NOPE. THAT'S ALL YOU, BUDDY.

WELL... I'VE STILL GOT TO GET PRIVATE JENSEN BACK. TALKING TO ANDY OR NOT.
AND WE'LL ALL HELP YOU. COME ON BACK TO THE ROOM, AND LET'S TALK ABOUT IT. MAKE SOME PLANS.
OKAY?

YES, SIR!

I TOTALLY WOULD'VE JUMPED, THORPE. YOU'RE A WEENIE.
OH, YOU JUST MADE MY LIST, GORDON.

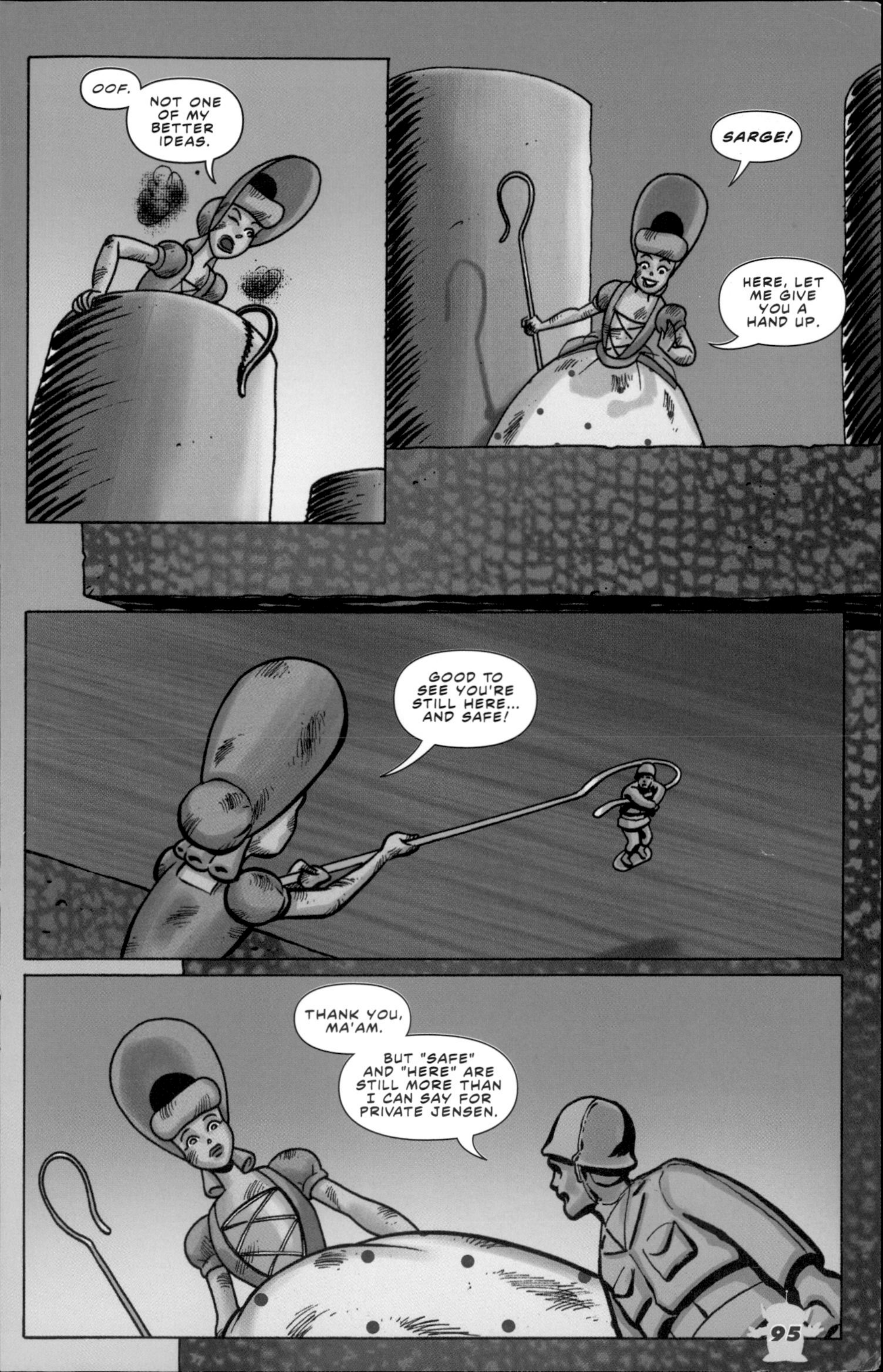
OOF.
NOT ONE OF MY BETTER IDEAS.
SARGE!
HERE, LET ME GIVE YOU A HAND UP.
GOOD TO SEE YOU'RE STILL HERE... AND SAFE!
THANK YOU, MA'AM.
BUT "SAFE" AND "HERE" ARE STILL MORE THAN I CAN SAY FOR PRIVATE JENSEN.

THAT AFTERNOON.
HEY GUYS!
GUESS WHAT HAPPENED AT SCHOOL TODAY?

IT WAS THE FUNNIEST THING --
-- I FOUND OUT I HAD A STOWAWAY!

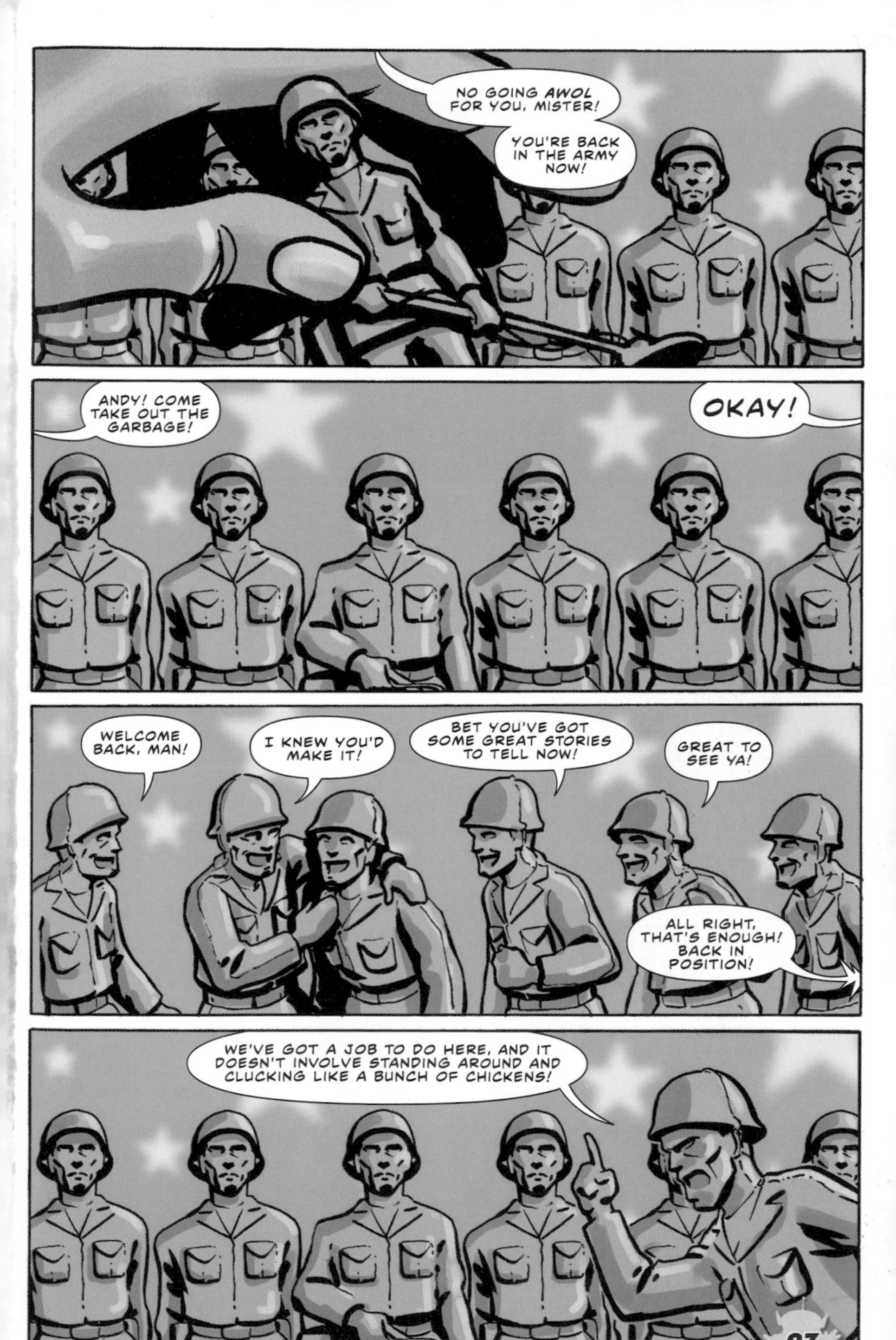
NO GOING AWOL FOR YOU, MISTER!
YOU'RE BACK IN THE ARMY NOW!
ANDY! COME TAKE OUT THE GARBAGE!
OKAY!
WELCOME BACK, MAN!
I KNEW YOU'D MAKE IT!
BET YOU'VE GOT SOME GREAT STORIES TO TELL NOW!
GREAT TO SEE YA!
ALL RIGHT, THAT'S ENOUGH! BACK IN POSITION!
WE'VE GOT A JOB TO DO HERE, AND IT DOESN'T INVOLVE STANDING AROUND AND CLUCKING LIKE A BUNCH OF CHICKENS!

NOW WHAT WAS IT YOU GUYS WERE ABOUT TO DO...?

OH -- RIGHT!
THE BRAVE FIGHTERS OF THE GAS GIANT PATROL STAND READY TO FACE THE NEXT IN A LONG LINE OF GAS GIANT MENACES!

LOOK OUT! IT'S A DEADLY DIRIGI-PIG!

WE'LL HAVE TO CALL IN A SPECIALIST...

CALLING CAPTAIN DEFLATORR! CAPTAIN DEFLATORR, FRONT AND CENTER!
THANKS, WOODY!